NEVER SAY MACBETH

SCRIPT & STAGE MANAGEMENT
MRS **Sheila FRONT**
PICTURES & COSTUMES & SETS BY
Charles FRONT ESQ

ANDRE DEUTSCH

For Jeremy and Rebecca who inspired this book.

First published in 1990 by
André Deutsch Limited
105–106 Great Russell Street, London WC1B 3LJ

ISBN 0 233 984542

Typeset by AKM Associates (UK) Ltd
Ajmal House, Hayes Road, Southall, London

Printed and bound in Belgium by
Proost International Book Production

GLOBE THEATRE

NEW STREET · SCRAGTHORPE

All communications regarding the business of the Theatre to be addressed to "The Manager"

Monday, November 2nd, 1895
FOR
TWO WEEKS ONLY

SIR MONTAGUE
WORTHINGTON-BROWNE
WITH
DAME NELLIE HARBOTTLE
AND THEIR COMPANY

MONDAY 2·9 WEDNESDAY 4·11 FRIDAY 6·13 Evenings Matinee-Wednesday	*The Great Tragedy by William Shakespeare* **MACBETH** Macbeth ... ... Sir Montague ... owne
TUESDAY 3·10 THURSDAY 5·12 Evenings	THE **RIV** By Richard Brinsley ...
SATURDAY 7·14 Evenings	**JU...** The Classic ... by Willia...

VACANCIES
APPLY WITH...
TO THE GLOBE THEATRE STAGE KEEPER

Jeremy Lamb had always wanted to be an actor.
When Sir Montague Worthington-Browne, the famous actor-manager arrived at the Globe Theatre, Jeremy, known as Jem, could hardly believe his luck. This was just the chance he had been waiting for. He made an appointment to see the great man.

Sir Montague and his wife, whose stage name was Dame Nellie Harbottle, knew how to make their audience laugh or cry. Though some said, rather unkindly, that their voices were too loud, their make-up too heavy, and their gestures too sweeping, theatre-goers adored them. From the stalls to the gallery, everyone clapped and cheered, as they took their curtain call.

They performed in plays by the great William Shakespeare. Sir Montague felt sure he looked distinguished in doublet and hose.

Dame Nellie enjoyed playing fine ladies in Restoration Comedy. She thought a powdered wig and lacy fan 'most becomin'.'

The day of Jem's appointment dawned.
Wandering nervously through the maze of winding corridors he
passed many dressing-rooms. At last he reached a heavy wooden
door bearing the name, Sir Montague Worthington-Browne. He
knocked shyly.
"Come in," boomed a loud voice. Taking a deep breath, Jem
entered the room and the great man introduced himself.

"I am Sir Montague
Worthington-Browne
with an e."
"I am Jeremy Lamb
without an e,"
whispered Jem.
"Come closer,"
said Sir Montague.
"So, you wish to become an
acTOR." He pronounced
the last syllable in a very
grand way. "But sweeping

the stage and pulling the curtains come first, playing Hamlet will come later."

"You may begin tomorrow if you wish," went on Sir Montague. "However, there are some warnings of a very serious nature I must give you. You see, we Thespians are superstitious people. We fear bad luck above all else. We dread anything that might spoil a theatrical performance.

"You must avoid doing certain things which are known to be unlucky. Be warned and remember:
   NEVER whistle in the dressing-room or wings.
   NEVER allow real flowers or peacock feathers on the stage.
   NEVER wear green. It is considered to be
an unlucky colour on the stage.

Above all, NEVER! NEVER! NEVER! SAY THE NAME . . . M * A * C * B * E * T * H!" He spelt the word slowly in a hoarse whisper, looking over his shoulder from time to time as if he feared even the spelling of it might bring disaster. "We are performing that great tragedy this season, but we always call it 'The Scottish Play'."

"And now," said Sir Montague, "I will take you to the Green Room to meet the rest of the company." Jem was introduced to the actors and actresses and also to Beerbohm, the theatre cat, a champion mouser.

Jem was also shown the rest of
the theatre by the master
carpenter, who was in charge of
the stage crew.
First they went beneath the
stage, a dark and dusty place
with a maze of levers, pulleys
and weights. The air was heavy
with the smell of sawdust, which
lay like a carpet on the floor. At
the sound of their footsteps, mice
scampered into the dark corners.

"I hope you've a head for heights," said the master carpenter as he lead the way up an iron spiral staircase which took them above the stage. "Most of us used to work on the big sailing ships, that's why we're called the crew." he explained.

Jem, looked around in amazement. The platform where they were standing overlooked the well-lit stage. Men were operating spot-lights which shone on the actors as they rehearsed. Jem really did feel as if he was on a sailing ship. He was surrounded by a forest of ropes, and huge canvas sheets bearing painted scenes swung above him. As he watched, Jem made up his mind. A life in the theatre was the only one for him.

Down below again, Jem stood in the wings beside the stage and, peering round the painted scenery, silently watched the rehearsal. As Dame Nellie's voice echoed around the empty auditorium, Jem dreamed of the great parts he would play one day.

Jem started to work at the Globe the following Monday.

On Friday the thirteenth the company was to perform 'The Scottish Play', the most dramatic piece in their repertoire. The impact on the audience was always amazing. Before the play Jem saw Sir Montague standing in the wings. He screwed up his courage and whispered, "I wish you luck with Macbeth tonight, sir."

Sir Montague paled under his greasepaint. His mouth fell open. His eyes stared wildly. "That name!" he bellowed, "you said . . . THAT NAME!"

"Sorry," Jem muttered feebly.

Sir Montague swept angrily past him, but said no more. Jem gave a low whistle of relief, quite forgetting that whistling was forbidden too. "That was a close shave," he whispered.

The play began. All seemed to be
going well until the final act. Dame
Nellie, her eyes raised to heaven, was
delivering her most dramatic lines.
Suddenly a mouse shot across the
stage with Beerbohm in hot pursuit.

Jem, aghast, forgot that he should not be seen by the audience and crawled onto the stage to catch the cat. Dame Nellie jumped onto a chair to stop the mouse from running up her nightdress. Sir Montague, forseeing disaster, rushed forward, to pull Jem back into the wings.

Confusion followed back stage. Someone
whispered urgently,
"Bring down the curtain!"
"Put out the lights!" hissed another. In the
pandemonium, a stagehand pulled the wrong lever
and Sir Montague, cloak whirling and arms
flailing, disappeared through a gaping trap door in
the stage.

The audience, who had come to see great tragedy, were
now witnessing grand farce.
They laughed till they cried.

They clapped and stamped their feet in approval, whilst, on stage, Sir Montague and Dame Nellie were soothed and comforted by the rest of the cast.

Later that night Jem
left the theatre with the
disgraced Beerbohm at his heels.
Jem knew how lucky he was that
Sir Montague and his wife had
agreed to give him another chance
and let him return to work the
following night.
"One thing is certain," thought
Jem, winking at Beerbohm,
"I'll NEVER say
M * A * C * B * E * T * H
again!"